Introduction

I magine a crop more versatile than the soybean, the cotton plant, and the Douglas fir tree put together…one whose products are interchangeable with those from timber or petroleum…one that grows like Jack's beanstalk with minimal tending. There *is* such a crop: industrial hemp.

Hemp was once indispensable to world commerce. New World colonists and traders were able to cross the Atlantic Ocean because the hemp ropes and sails of their ships, unlike other natural fibers, resisted salt damage. Not so long ago, it was inconceivable for an economy to function without hemp. The 1913 *Yearbook of the*

Years.	Imports.	Production in United States.	Total.
	Tons.	*Tons.*	*Tons.*
1876 to 1880.......	459	7,396	7,855
1881 to 1885.......	5,393	5,421	10,814
1886 to 1890.......	10,427	8,270	18,697
1891 to 1895.......	4,962	5,631	10,593
1896 to 1900.......	4,985	5,177	10,162
1901 to 1905.......	4,577	6,175	10,752
1906 to 1910.......	6,375	5,150	11,525
1911 to 1913.......	5,982	5,100	11,082

Historic chart of hemp production from 1876 to 1913 (source: 1913 Yearbook of the U.S. Department of Agriculture).

ro-fiber composites • animal bedding • archery strings

U.S. Department of Agriculture called hemp "the oldest cultivated fiber plant," mentioned how the crop improves the land, and said that it yields "one of the strongest and most durable fibers of commerce."

Then, in 1937, fiber hemp fell victim to the anti-drug sentiment of the times when the U.S. Congress passed the Marihuana Tax Act. The intent of this law was to prohibit the use of marijuana, but it created so much red tape that the production of industrial hemp became nearly impossible. Now hemp's natural fiber and seed oil were no longer available to compete with wood pulp, cotton, and such newly patented petroleum products as inks, paints, plastics, solvents, sealants, and synthetic fabrics.

The fact is that hemp grown for fiber, whether by George Washington in 1790, by Kentucky growers in 1935, or by English farmers in 1994, has never contained psychoactive qualities. If one were to roll leaves from an industrial hemp plant into a cigarette and smoke them, no euphoric effects would be experienced even if a thousand hemp cigarettes were smoked. The potentially psychoactive chemical in hemp is delta-9 tetrahydrocannabinol (THC). A plant cultivated for marijuana has a 3 to 15 percent THC content or more, while industrial hemp generally contains one percent or less.

How do governments continue to justify the prohibition of hemp farming? Their primary justification is that the licensing of industrial-hemp farms will lead to an increased supply of illegal marijuana. Yet the vast fields of fiber hemp grown from France to Russia have never been—*could* never be—used for drug trafficking. (Incidentally, stands of fiber hemp are planted very closely together, and look completely different from cultivated marijuana.)

Hemp's versatility was explained in a 1938 *Popular Mechanics* magazine article, "New Billion-Dollar Crop": "Hemp is the standard fiber of the world…and can be used to produce more than 25,000 products." The list running throughout this book provides a sam-

INDUSTRIAL HEMP

Practical Products—
Paper to Fabric to Cosmetics

Table of Contents

Introduction 3

Chapter 1 Hemp's Historical Role in Commerce 6

Chapter 2 The Earth's Premier Renewable Resource . . . 15

Chapter 3 Hemp's 25,000 Practical Products 24

Chapter 4 Today's Hemp Industry 31

Chapter 5 Jobs and Business Opportunities 40

Chapter 6 The Next Step 43

Glossary 46

Resources . . . . Inside Back Cover

Editor and Publisher: John W. Roulac
Associate Editor: Sonia Nordenson
Technical Editors: Geoff Kime and Joe Strobel of Hempline, Inc., Mike Ravnitzky of Industrial Fabrics Association International, John Birrenbach of the Institute for Hemp, Gero Leson of nova Institute, Don Wirtshafter of Ohio Hempery, Inc., and David P. West, Ph.D.
Cover Design: Robert Howard
Layout: White Light Publishing
Printing: Optima Graphics, Inc.
Paper: American Hemp Mercantile

HEMPTECH would like to thank everyone who provided inspiration and assistance in creating this book, including: Isabele Adams, Angela Armstrong, Craig Benton, Lynn Blackman, Jari Chevalier, Roger Christie, Tara Crowley, Tina Davis, Gale Glenn, Elise Harvey, Jack Herer, Chuck Hinsch, Scott and Meredith Manhard, Karen Newell, Dan Poynter, Elizabeth Roulac, Phil Roulac, Steve Roulac, Dave Seber, Holly Stasinis, Tim Thomas, Carl Tolbert, Akiva Werbalowsky, and Jan Wilson.

First printing June 1995
0 9 8 7 6 5 4 3 2 1

ISBN 1-886874-00-X
CIP 94-96890

If your local bookstore, retailer, or catalog company is sold out of *Industrial Hemp*, contact HEMPTECH at P.O. Box 820, Ojai, CA 93024-0820, (805) 646-HEMP.

HEMPTECH ™ ℠
Industrial Hemp Information Specialists

pling of hemp's cornucopia of products. Chapter 3 will highlight major hemp-product categories, from construction materials and cosmetics to paper, textiles, and even plastics.

Industrial hemp is a valuable, low-cost biological resource that can be grown in most climates. It is a hardy plant whose rapid growth and high resistance to diseases largely eliminate the need for costly herbicides or pesticides. Hemp can play an important role in rural economic development: new jobs and businesses can be created to produce hemp products, for both local consumption and marketing to other regions.

In his October 30, 1988, editorial in California's most conservative newspaper, *The Orange County Register*, senior columnist Alan Bock stated that "Since 1937, about half the forests in the world have been cut down to make paper. If hemp had not been outlawed, most would still be standing, oxygenating the planet."

Major hemp-growing countries today include China, England, France, Holland, Hungary, and Russia. Nations that ban hemp production are missing an important economic opportunity. Australia, Canada, and Germany, although they still prohibit hemp farming, now allow selected farms to plant hemp for research purposes.

In the U.S., a promising crack in the "hemp wall" appeared in November of 1994 when the Governor of Kentucky, Brereton C. Jones, announced the formation of a new task force to evaluate the feasibility of, in the Governor's words, "...hemp and related fiber crops production as a supplement crop to tobacco."

As this book goes to print, State Senator Lloyd Casey of Colorado is introducing the Hemp Production Act of 1995 for consideration by the Colorado State legislature.

Hemp will be like the Internet, which two years ago wasn't even on the corporate or government radar screen. Two years from now, knowledge of hemp and its products will have spread to homes and businesses throughout the world.

1

Hemp's Historical Role in Commerce

In 1791, Thomas Jefferson said, "Hemp is of first necessity to the commerce and marine, in other words, to the wealth and protection of the Country." Few people today realize that hemp, genus *Cannabis sativa L.* of the mulberry family, was once so vital to world commerce.

Thomas Jefferson.

Throughout the world for more than 6,000 years (some historians estimate 10,000 years), hemp has been relied upon to supply a wide range of essential products. In 4500 B.C. in China, hemp or *ma* was used for making ropes and fishnets. China later developed the world's first paper industry by using hemp to make scrolls. The great writings of Confucius and Lao Tsu were transcribed on hemp paper, which doesn't turn yellow or brittle, and thus that wisdom was handed down from generation to generation. China also cultivated the fiber for hempen cloth, and used hemp seed for food and oil.

Chinese ma symbol.

Hemp Travels to Europe
Hemp seeds and the knowledge of their use spread from Asia to the Mediterranean and on through Europe. In the area of Stuttgart, Germany, hemp-based rope and fabric dated at around 400 B.C.

have been found. In 1886 *The Origin of Plants* stated, "Hiero II, King of Syracuse (270 B.C.), purchased hemp in Gaul for the cordage of his vessels."

In the 14th century, the traditional Chinese art of making paper from hemp and flax rags arrived in Germany via Italy. The *canvas* on which Renaissance artists painted took its name from the word *Cannabis*. Hemp's heyday in Germany was the 17th century, when about 375,000 acres were under cultivation. From the 16th to the 18th century, hemp and flax are known to have been the major fiber crops in Asia, Russia, Europe, and North America. Spanish, French, British, German, and Dutch trading ships, like the ships that brought colonists to America, were rigged with hemp ropes and sails. In the mid-1800s, France had more than 800,000 acres of hemp under cultivation. According to the 1913 *Yearbook of the U.S. Department of Agriculture*, "In 1846 M. Herbert sent from China to the Museum of Paris some seeds of the "tsing-ma," great hemp of China…the plants…grew tall, some of them measuring 21 feet."

Hemp Growing Required

In the North American colonies, hemp quickly became an indispensable raw material. Many of the American colonists' Bibles and maps were printed on hemp paper, and much of their lamp oil came from pressed

Early ships relied on hemp sails and rigging.

hemp seeds. Hemp production was so important for commerce that in 1640 the Governor of Connecticut declared that every citizen must grow the plant. In the 1700s and 1800s, Russia's number-one trading crop was hemp, which supplied sails and ropes for American, Canadian, and European ships. The high value placed on hemp helped create the first recycling business in America: old hemp and flax clothing, rags, and sails were converted into paper. Through

George Washington

trade with Spain, hemp rope and linen factories were developed in Mexico as well as in Central and South America.

America's founding fathers were strong advocates of a hemp-based economy for their new country. In fact, George Washington and Thomas Jefferson were themselves long-time hemp farmers.

From a 1765 letter:
"I am prepared to deliver…hemp in your port watered and prepared according to the Act of Parliament."
—George Washington

The first two drafts of the Declaration of Independence were written on hemp paper. The Daughters of the American Revolution sewed hemp linens for the Continental Army, without which more Revolutionary soldiers might have frozen to death at the battle of Valley Forge. Hemp rope, which is extremely strong, was used to rig the Early American Navy and Merchant Marine ships. In regions where hemp was prominent—such as Hempstead, New York, and Hemphill, Texas — dozens of towns were actually named after hemp.

The harvest of a hemp field (source: 1913 Yearbook of the USDA).

A hemp handbrake (source: 1913 Yearbook of the USDA).

A hemp machine brake (source: 1913 Yearbook of the USDA).

A Technology Breakthrough

By the end of the 19th century, hemp's vital role in commerce was in decline throughout the world. Technologies such as the cotton gin had greatly cut labor costs in the cotton industry, whereas the hemp industry was not competitive due to a lack of mechanized harvesting and processing. At that time, only about 25 percent of the hemp stalk was useable. The remaining inner hurds (the shorter fibers) were burned in the fields as waste.

In 1916, there was a major breakthrough for the hemp industry. The U.S. Department of Agriculture produced Bulletin Number 404, "Hemp Hurds as Paper Making Material," which read in part: "This bulletin is printed on paper manufactured from hemp hurds," and declared that a new, labor-saving decorticating machine would slash hemp's labor costs, improve paper quality, and protect forests by providing a low-cost and abundant source to fill the world's growing need for paper. Hemp production, the bulletin said, would once again be America's largest agricultural industry.

The harvest of a turn-of-the-century hemp field (source: The Reign of Law: A Tale of the Kentucky Hemp Fields, *James Lane Allen, 1900).*

From the 1880s through the 1930s, a variety of decorticating patents were applied for and granted. In 1917, such a patent was issued to inventor George W. Schlichten. Finally, with Schlichten's innovation, there was a machine that economically separated the hemp fibers from the previously unusable hurds. Don Wirtshafter, the author of *The Schlichten Papers*, wrote, "It was clearly the work of a genius, solving an age-old problem. Hundreds of inventors, including Thomas Jefferson, a hemp farmer, had tried to invent an efficient process to gather all the useful fibers. Before the invention of the decorticator, it took tedious work to break the tough stalks into shape for spinning into yarn. The new technology reduced labor costs by a factor of at least 100." The hemp industry was now in a strong economic position, able to use 95 percent of the stalk versus the former 25 percent, while slashing labor costs as well.

Hydrocarbon or Carbohydrate?

The outlook for hemp seemed promising. New allies emerged to promote the use of agricultural crops as raw materials for American industry. David P. West, Ph.D., plant breeder, hemp historian, and the author of *Fiber Wars*, says: "In the 1930s, a new science was developing called 'chemurgy' (a term coined by William Hale), the bringing together of agriculture and the organic chemical industry. Hale was a biochemist with Dow Chemical, which had its roots in agriculture. The chemurgy catch phrase was:

> *Anything that can be made from a hydrocarbon*
> *can be made from a carbohydrate.*

"Hale joined forces with the American Farm Bureau and Henry Ford to promote the vision of farm products replacing imported oil for fuels, lubricants, and synthetic fibers."

Henry Ford introduced an automobile that ran on fuels derived from hemp and other agricultural-based sources. Even the fenders were made of hemp, wheat, straw, and synthetic plastics. Ford said his vision was "to grow automobiles from the soil."

What happened after that, we may never know. Historians have speculated about why the agricultural chemurgy industry fell out of favor. Petroleum was in abundant supply, and therefore less costly. Perhaps another factor in hemp's downfall was its rural, decentralized approach. Its primary economic beneficiaries were

An early Ford with hemp fenders.

farmers and smaller regional manufacturers. In that era of big government and big business, the centralized structure of the petrochemical and timber industries seemed to have a broader appeal.

Petroleum technologies promised a new age of synthetics, and people were attracted to the novelty of such products. Sixty years later, the world is still living with the consequences of pollution and economic dependence that synthetics have brought.

During the 1920s and 1930s, films such as *Reefer Madness* began to appear. Warnings such as "Killer Weed, Marihuana, the Greatest Menace to Society Ever Known" were seen in newspapers.

In 1937, the anti-drug sentiment brought the Marihuana Tax Act before Congress. In congressional hearings, the American Medical Association testified against the act, emphasizing the importance of hemp for use in numerous pharmaceuticals. The National Seed Oil Institute also lobbied strongly, pleading that hemp oil was of vital importance in the production of paints and resins and in other industrial processes. Yet that year the Marihuana Tax Act, effectively prohibiting hemp farming, was passed.

Until that time, hemp factories had been expanding production. On December 31, 1937, *The Winona Republican*, a Minnesota newspaper, printed an article stating, "The Chempco plant produces more than a carload of hemp fiber per day and more than three carloads of the woody material called hemp hurds. This woody material is ground into a 'flour' which can be made into a wide variety of compositions." The article further said that hemp was used to produce fine writing papers as well as hard plastics for manufacturing "telephone sets." The 1937 congressional bill did not ban such production, but further evidence discovered by West indicates that the new industry in Minnesota was harassed out of business by narcotics agents. West has obtained the testimony of the son of the president of one of the Minnesota companies (Cannabis, Inc.), who states categorically that government red tape over the marijuana issue caused the industry's demise. By 1940, the Minnesota companies had ceased to exist. Their innovative decorticating technology would have to wait for another era.

> In 1938, *Popular Mechanics* magazine published the article "New Billion-Dollar Crop," which informed readers: "American farmers are promised a new cash crop, all because a machine has been invented which solves a problem more than 6,000 years old. The machine which makes this possible is designed for removing the fiber from the rest of the stalk, making hemp fiber available for use without a prohibitive amount of human labor. Hemp is the standard fiber of the world. It has great tensile strength and durability. It is used to produce more than 5,000 textile products ranging from rope to fine laces, and the woody 'hurds' remaining after the fibers have been removed can be used to produce more than 25,000 products, ranging from dynamite to cellophane. It can be grown in any state of the union."

Hemp for Victory

Hemp briefly reemerged on the American scene in 1942, when the U.S. Army and Department of Agriculture released their "Hemp for Victory" campaign, featuring a film (now available on video) rallying American farmers to grow hemp for wartime needs. The war had cut off the importation of fibers for textiles and rope, and by 1943 over 100,000 acres of hemp were being grown in the U.S. For its part, Germany produced a book encouraging German farmers to plant hemp. When World War II ended, the U.S. Government canceled virtually all hemp-farming permits. No one seemed to question:

Scene aboard a Navy ship, from the 1942 U.S. government film Hemp for Victory.

If hemp was such an important wartime resource, why not benefit from it during times of peace?

In June of 1991, Jim Young, technical editor of *Pulp and Paper*, wrote an editorial entitled "It's Time to Reconsider Hemp" in which he reported that "United States hemp-growing restrictions were set aside to meet material shortages during World War II. They should now at least be modified to meet pending shortages of fiber, energy, and environmental quality. Tradition, if not federal law, is on the side of hemp."

2

The Earth's Premier Renewable Resource

As the worldwide population increases, the demand for resources also increases. For example, in the coming decades China's economic plans may call for an annual consumption of fiber and fuel resources similar to that of the United States. In Germany, the term "bioresource hemp" is used to describe this useful plant as a biological resource to meet these needs. The law of supply and demand is creating a significant market opportunity for hemp. Later in this chapter, we'll discuss the role of hemp as a bioresource from three different perspectives: those of the farmer, the manufacturer/processor, and the individual citizen.

A Worldwide Fiber Shortage

Now as during World War II, the world faces a fiber shortage. In 1994, resource shortages caused North American commodity prices for recycled paper and plastic to skyrocket. There is an ever-increasing need to find fiber for paper and construction products. With one-half million acres of hemp fiber grown annually to meet this need in nations such as China, England, and France, the current prohibition in Australia, Canada, Germany, and the United States is hard to justify. In this era of global trade, nations with obsolescent market barriers that prohibit hemp production needlessly limit the economic and environmental well-being of their citizens.

The annual world consumption of paper has risen from 14 million tons in 1913 to over 250 million tons in the 1990s. So much for the predicted paperless office! A September 1994 *Wall Street Journal* article stated: "…restrictions on logging in federal forests will boost prices of virgin pulp used to make paper. Pete Grogan, manager of market development for Weyerhaeuser Corporation's recycling unit, said, 'We're concerned there might be paper shortages this decade.'" In the fall of 1994, two of the largest paper producers in the world, International Paper and Champion International, actually had to declare week-long moratoriums when they could not accept new paper orders. In the United States alone, the demand for fiber is greater than the combined demand for all steel and plastic products. In response to this need, people around the world are rallying for a return to hemp, the earth's premier renewable resource.

Farmers

From a farmer's perspective, hemp is a low-maintenance crop to grow, and one whose advantages are beginning to be recognized in the agricultural community. In the October 19, 1994, *Farmer's Pride* newspaper, Ed Logsdon, the Commissioner of Agriculture for the State of Kentucky, said, "It's time to look at producing hemp on a commercial basis."

A farmer cutting his hemp (source: 1913 Yearbook of the USDA).

The following appeared in the George Lower article "Flax and Hemp, From the Seed to the Loom," in the February 1938 issue of *Mechanical Engineering*.

"Hemp, the strongest of the vegetable fibers, gives the greatest production per acre and requires the least attention. It not only requires no weeding, but also kills off all the weeds, and leaves the soil in splendid condition for the following crop. This, irrespective of its own monetary value, makes it a desirable crop to grow. Because hemp is such a strong fiber, it requires specialized harvesting and processing equipment.... The hemp industry has to make further progress in this area before large crops can be grown and processed. Several types of machines are available in this country for harvesting hemp. One of these was brought out several years ago by International Harvester Company. Paint and lacquer manufacturers are interested in hemp-seed oil, which is a good drying agent. When markets have been developed with the products now being wasted...hemp will prove both to the farmer and the public, it is the most profitable and desirable crop that can be grown and one that can make American mills independent of imports."

The Effects of Farming With Chemicals

Much of the fiber for textiles currently comes from cotton. *The Wall Street Journal* has reported that many Asian cotton farmers use up to seven times the directed amount of pesticides for their crops. In the U.S., about half the pesticides used today are sprayed on cotton plants. The June 1994 issue of *National Geographic* stated that "in California alone some 6,000 tons of pesticides and defoliants are used on cotton in a single year." Much of the groundwater tested in agricultural regions around the world has been contaminated by runoff from pesticides, herbicides, and fertilizers. The potential health hazards that pesticides present are well documented. According to the book *World Medicine* by Tom Mount, "farmers in the corn belt have the highest incidence of leukemia, prostate, and pancreatic cancer deaths," attributable to "the introduction of chlorinated hydrocarbon pesticides in 1945." Perhaps farmers have felt they've had no choice but to use these chemicals, given the realities of supporting their families in today's economy. But these realities are in the process of change.

Industrial hemp gives farmers a crop that produces a high-quality fiber with few synthetic chemicals, if any. Since hemp plants grow 6 to 16 feet tall in 70 to 110 days, farmers of large and small acreages alike can shade out weeds and thus eliminate the use of costly herbicides. Hemp yields three to eight tons of dry stalk per acre, depending on climate and variety. After hemp is harvested, the field is left virtually weed-free for the next crop. This last fact alone will save farmers untold thousands of dollars, while improving water quality.

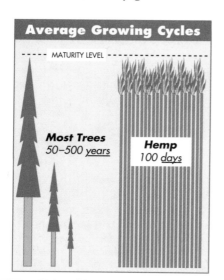

Average Growing Cycles

----- MATURITY LEVEL -----

Most Trees
50–500 <u>years</u>

Hemp
100 <u>days</u>

Further, hemp grown in North America requires no pesticides. (In damper European climates, hemp may be subject to minor fungal diseases that are unlikely to occur in North American climates.) Hemp grown for high yield will require equal or greater fertilization than wheat or corn. Consumer trends in foods and textiles indicate a growing demand for products certified to be organic. Sustainable or organic growers can fertilize their hemp crops with biofertilizers such as compost, manures, and biosolids, and by planting nitrogen-fixing crops such as peas, beans, or clovers in rotation with the hemp. Also, hemp tops and leaves, when returned to the field, add fertility to the soil.

With the tobacco industry in decline, there is a strong interest among tobacco farmers in the cultivation of hemp. Yet there are still several obstacles facing potential hemp farmers. Besides the fact that hemp cannot yet be legally grown, it's an unfamiliar crop for farmers, and most hemp markets are still in their infancy. The majority of the hemp grown today relies on plentiful labor rather than mechanized harvesting equipment. In developed countries, investments in the designing of new farm machinery will be needed before large-scale plantings will be cost-efficient.

Hemp-Farming Benefits

• **Naturally hardy** •
In the Midwest, large wild stands of hemp are common.

• **Biological weed control** •
Hemp outruns weeds, creating a virtually weed-free field for the next crop.

• **Low input costs** •
No pesticides or herbicides required.

• **Adds value to the regional economy** •
Provides valuable materials for local manufacturing.

furniture • futons • geotextiles • gloves • glues •

Hemp-Seed Facts

The U.S. Department of Agriculture's National Seed Laboratory in Fort Collins, Colorado, explains that, because hemp was not considered an important fiber resource, the government's hemp-seed stock was abandoned. Thus, it has been lost to future generations, and, as a result, U.S. farmers will have to rely on imported seed stock for initial plantings.

The 12-country European Economic Community (EEC) permits farmers to grow hemp certified to contain 0.3 percent THC or less. France is the major supplier of the seeds for such low-THC varieties. A better standard would be one percent THC or less, allowing for the cultivation of more productive Chinese and Eastern European strains, which range from 0.3 to one percent. As was explained in the Introduction, these seed varieties produce plants with no psychoactive properties.

Manufacturers and Processors

Hemp's versatility yields a range of materials that can be processed into thousands of valuable products: fiber and hurds (the core of the stem) from the stalk, and seed, seed oil, and seed cake (crushed seed). The U.S. government, while not officially researching hemp, is advocating the use of crops to replace nonrenewable manufacturing resources. The kenaf plant, native to Africa and currently harvested throughout the Southern United States, has been found by the USDA and by private corporations to produce high-quality papers and fiberboard products. Much of the kenaf research is applicable to hemp. Robert Armstrong of the USDA Alternative Agricultural Research and Commercialization Center says, "We are beginning to recognize that these (agricultural crops) are renewable materials that can be used in a vast area of industrial products from plastics to lubricants."

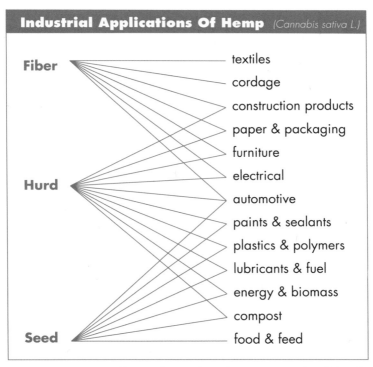

Industrial Applications Of Hemp *(Cannabis sativa L.)*

Fiber
Hurd
Seed

- textiles
- cordage
- construction products
- paper & packaging
- furniture
- electrical
- automotive
- paints & sealants
- plastics & polymers
- lubricants & fuel
- energy & biomass
- compost
- food & feed

Source: C & S Specialty Builder's Supply Inc., Advanced Composites From Annual Fibers™, *Harrisburg, OR.*

While hemp has a long history, it is currently a kind of agricultural Rip Van Winkle, just starting to reawaken after its 60-year sleep. It is now, in effect, a new resource for manufacturers and

industrial coatings • industrial oils • insulation materials

processors. Like any new resource, it will require innovative processing technology, such as modernizing the decorticating machine that boosted the hempstalk yield more than six decades ago.

Textiles and fine writing papers are two markets for hemp's higher-quality long bast fibers. The remaining hurds can be ground into a "flour" for use in thousands of products, including fiberboard, packaging, diapers, etc. The hemp seed can be processed into many nutritious food products. Hemp-seed oil offers promising opportunities for use in cosmetics, nutrition, printing inks, and industrial coatings. The remaining crushed seed is also valuable for food, including animal feed.

	Fiberboard	Paper	Textiles
North American Industry Demand for New Fiber Sources	Very High	High	Medium*
Manufacturer's Ability to Use Hemp With Current Equipment	Yes	Yes (with additional modifications)	Yes** (with major modifications)

   *   There is a growing consumer interest in natural organic fibers.
  ** Imported hemp fabric already spun can be sewn using current technologies. See Textiles, page 26, for facts on new hemp cottonization process.

The Benefits of Tree-Free Paper

Hemp and kenaf make possible the production and use of tree-free paper, from which there are several environmental advantages to be gained. One acre of annually grown hemp may spare up to four acres of forest from the current practice of clear-cutting. Compared to wood, fewer chemicals are required to convert low-lignin tree-free fibers to pulp. Using fewer chemicals reduces waste-water contamination. Because most plant fibers are naturally a whiter color than wood, they require less bleaching, and, in some cases, none. Less bleaching results in less dioxin and fewer chemical by-products being generated by the papermaking process.

Individual Citizens

Most hemp products are high-quality, long-lasting, and processed in an ecologically responsible manner. Once growing restrictions are lifted, hemp products will be priced at levels similar to those of competing products, if not below them.

Many existing products, such as cotton, rely on farm chemicals manufactured at huge petrochemical refineries. These facilities create some of the worst pollution of air, soil, and water in the world. Underprivileged people find affordable housing near these facilities and, due to their impoverished circumstances, must live with toxicity. When we support the use of these chemicals through our purchases, we send the message: "Please continue to produce these products, no matter how you do it or who it harms." By purchasing hemp products, we support farmers, while reducing the amount of toxins released into the environment.

As thousands of communities around the world strengthen their economies with hemp, we will begin to see positive impacts on our global environment. Oil consumption will drop, due to a reduction in the use of synthetic chemicals and in the number of trucks and tankers carrying products around the globe. As an added environmental benefit, the restoration of our forests and the planting of millions of acres of fast-growing hemp will add life-giving oxygen to the atmosphere.

3

Hemp's 25,000 Practical Products

In 1938, *Popular Mechanics* magazine stated, "Over 25,000 products can be manufactured from hemp, from cellophane to dynamite." Since it would be impossible to list all of these here, this chapter provides an overview of some of the major hemp products. Naturally, time will tell which of hemp's many potential products will prove to have an edge over products made from other materials.

The fiber-composite industry, which manufactures fiberboard, paneling, and plywood, is the largest potential market for hemp fibers. At current tree-harvesting levels, composite mills need to find an alternative fiber source to stay in business. These factories can substitute hemp for wood and still use existing production equipment.

Hemp jeans, shirts, and hats are becoming fashionable from Hamburg to Los Angeles to Tokyo. *The London Financial Times* reported in an October 26, 1994, article: "...fibre hemp...is making a comeback in Europe and the U.S. as an ecologically friendly raw material for clothing and paper." Hemp cosmetics such as lip balm, salves, soaps, and massage oil are gaining in popularity. Also, the potential use of hemp as a biomass fuel source is receiving renewed interest.

Composites

The products known as composites, including paneling, medium-density fiberboard, trusses, and support beams, comprise the fastest-growing segment of the wood-products industry. Washington State University's preeminent Wood Composite Laboratory has

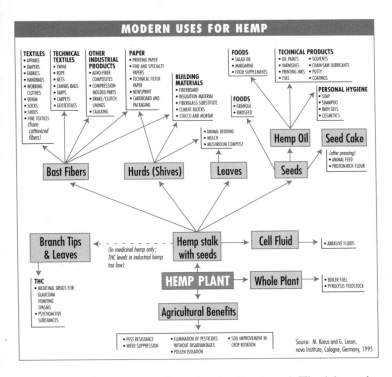

MODERN USES FOR HEMP

TEXTILES
- APPAREL
- DIAPERS
- FABRICS
- HANDBAGS
- WORKING CLOTHES
- DENIM
- SOCKS
- SHOES
- FINE TEXTILES (from cottonized fibers)

TECHNICAL TEXTILES
- TWINE
- ROPE
- NETS
- CANVAS BAGS
- TARPS
- CARPETS
- GEOTEXTILES

OTHER INDUSTRIAL PRODUCTS
- AGRO-FIBER COMPOSITES
- COMPRESSION-MOLDED PARTS
- BRAKE/CLUTCH LININGS
- CAULKING

PAPER
- PRINTING PAPER
- FINE AND SPECIALTY PAPERS
- TECHNICAL FILTER PAPER
- NEWSPRINT
- CARDBOARD AND PACKAGING

BUILDING MATERIALS
- FIBERBOARD
- INSULATION MATERIAL
- FIBERGLASS SUBSTITUTE
- CEMENT BLOCKS
- STUCCO AND MORTAR

FOODS
- SALAD OIL
- MARGARINE
- FOOD SUPPLEMENTS

FOODS
- GRANOLA
- BIRDSEED

TECHNICAL PRODUCTS
- OIL PAINTS
- VARNISHES
- PRINTING INKS
- FUEL
- SOLVENTS
- CHAIN-SAW LUBRICANTS
- PUTTY
- COATINGS

PERSONAL HYGIENE
- SOAP
- SHAMPOO
- BATH GELS
- COSMETICS

- ANIMAL BEDDING
- MULCH
- MUSHROOM COMPOST

Hemp Oil

Seed Cake
- (after pressing)
- ANIMAL FEED
- PROTEIN-RICH FLOUR

Bast Fibers — **Hurds (Shives)** — **Leaves** — **Seeds**

Branch Tips & Leaves

(In medicinal hemp only; THC levels in industrial hemp too low)

Hemp stalk with seeds — **Cell Fluid**
- ABRASIVE FLUIDS

THC
- MEDICINAL DRUGS FOR:
  GLAUCOMA
  VOMITING
  SPASMS
- PSYCHOACTIVE SUBSTANCES

HEMP PLANT — **Whole Plant**
- BOILER FUEL
- PYROLYSIS FEEDSTOCK

Agricultural Benefits

- PEST RESISTANCE
- WEED SUPPRESSION
- ELIMINATION OF PESTICIDES WITHOUT DISADVANTAGES
- POLLEN ISOLATION
- SOIL IMPROVEMENT IN CROP ROTATION

Source: M. Karus and G. Leson, nova Institute, Cologne, Germany, 1995

tested hemp for use in medium-density fiberboard. The lab results show that hemp is twice as strong as wood. According to lab director Tom Maloney, "The use of hemp fiber in multidensity fiberboard and other composites looks very promising."

C&S Specialty Building Supply of Harrisburg, Oregon, is currently researching hemp composite boards as well as other alternatives to the use of formaldehyde as a glue in composite products.

Poland and other Eastern European countries presently operate low-tech hemp-pressboard production facilities.

Cosmetics

Numerous cosmetic products can be manufactured using the oil extracted from hemp seeds. Research has shown that hemp oil assists the body's natural ability to heal, both externally and internally. Because of its ability to restore and

Sample from a hemp-fiber composite board manufactured in Poland.

moisten skin, hemp oil is becoming popular for use as a massage oil and in lip balms, soaps, and lotions. Its essential fatty acids are readily absorbed into skin cells. When combined with herbs, hemp-oil salve assists in healing skin irritations, insect bites, and minor cuts.

Feed

The hemp seed has long been popular as a feed stock for a variety of animals. Birds are especially attracted to the hemp seed for its superior nutritional qualities. To this day, most birdseed mixes contain hemp seed. After hemp seed is crushed to extract the oil, the remaining seed cake is approximately 25 percent protein, and makes excellent feed for domestic animals as well as for cows and chickens.

Foodstuffs

Hemp seed, the hulls of which contain about 25 percent protein, is a nutritious food source, high in calcium, magnesium, phosphorus, potassium, and vitamin A. Like soybeans, hemp seed can be made into numerous food products, yet it is easier to digest. The seeds can be ground, soaked, or crushed for their oil content. After the seeds are crushed, the remaining seed cake can be processed into a flour for making high-quality breads, cakes, pastas, and cookies. In Europe, traditional hemp-seed dishes such as Silesian hemp soup are still enjoyed.

A nourishing confection can be made from hemp seeds, nuts, and honey. Nondairy cheese, milk, and even ice cream can be made by soaking and processing the hemp seed. Udo Erasmus, Ph.D., the author of *Fats and Oils: The Complete Guide to Fats and Oils in Health and Nutrition,* states that "hemp butter puts peanut butter to shame for nutritional value." Many European cultures still grind hemp seeds to make this butter.

The oil can be taken as a nutritional supplement similar to flax-seed oil, or can be used in salad dressings and other oil-based recipes. At a volume level of 81 percent, hemp oil is the richest known source of polyunsaturated essential fatty acids (the "good" fats). Research by Donald Wirtshafter has confirmed that hemp oil also contains gamma linoleic acid (GLA), a very rare nutrient also found in borage, black currant, primrose oil, and mother's milk. These essential fatty acids are needed for healthy skin, hair, and eyes, and for overall physical health.

Hemp seed and its oil contain no psychoactive properties whatsoever. In countries where hemp cultivation is prohibited, imported seed must be sterilized in steam for 15 minutes to make their germination impossible. The sterilized seed can then legally be used. Unfortunately, this sterilization of hemp seed accelerates rancidity, and makes the seed and its products more expensive.

Insulation

Hemp can be processed into a variety of insulation products that are safer than fiberglass and easy to install. A French firm is converting hemp hurds into a fluffy cellulose product that is blown into walls and attic air spaces, or placed there in bags.

Paints and Sealants

Until the 1930s, linseed and hemp oils made up the majority of all resins, paints, shellacs, and varnishes. With the advent of less-expensive petroleum-based paints and sealants, combined with the government hemp ban of 1937, hemp products disappeared from the marketplace. As long as synthetic products are less costly, plant-based paints and sealants are not likely to reappear.

Paper

This book is printed on tree-free hemp paper. Hemp has a yield-per-acre several times higher than that of trees. Its longer fibers create high-quality paper for books, magazines, and stationary, while the shorter fibers make excellent newspaper, tissue paper, and packaging materials. Until the late nineteenth century, the world relied on annual crops such as hemp, flax, and cotton for all these kinds of paper.

The low lignin content of hemp fiber allows for environmentally friendly bleaching, without the use of harsh chlorine compounds. Hemp paper resists decomposition, and is not subject to the age-related yellowing of wood-derived papers. In fact, hemp paper more than 1,500 years old has recently been found. Because of the strength of hemp fiber, paper made of hemp can be recycled several times more than paper made of wood. Rising populations, combined with accelerated deforestation, are motivating the paper industry to explore nonwood fiber sources. Two German mills have begun to produce hemp paper, and Kimberly-Clark, a United States Fortune 500 company, operates a mill in France to produce hemp paper for Bibles and cigarettes. Emerging pulping technologies will allow for pulping of the entire stalk (including the hurds), significantly increasing the per-acre pulp yield.

Pharmaceuticals

In the early 20th century, hemp extracts were commonly used by major pharmaceutical companies such as Eli Lilly to make a variety of medicines. Perhaps that is why the American Medical Association testified against the prohibition of hemp at the 1937 congressional hearings to ban the crop. It is becoming increasingly well known that hemp oil's high vitamin and essential-fatty-acid content assists the body's natural healing ability.

Plastics

There are three different ways that hemp can be used to manufacture plastic products: (1) The hurds are easily processed into cellophane packaging material (plant-based cellophane, common until the 1930s, is still in use today). (2) The hurds can be blended in a 50-percent hemp (or kenaf) and 50-percent recycled-plastic mixture for manufacturing injection-molded products. (3) The seed oil can be converted into a valuable plastic resin. Each of these product types will require further research and development before being launched in the marketplace.

As was mentioned previously, Henry Ford even used hemp to build car doors and fenders. Cargill, the largest agricultural-based company in the U.S., manufactures a line of 100-percent-plant-derived spoons, forks, and plates (primarily from corn), as well as coatings that can be used for such products as paper cups.

Plant-based plastics such as hemp and corn can be completely biodegradable. The use of hemp for plastics will reduce oil consumption and the processing of petrochemicals. Plastic packaging (the kind found inside cereal boxes, for example) made from hemp could be composted at home, eliminating some of the high cost of landfilling or of recycling petroleum-based plastics.

Textiles

The third-largest industry in the world is the manufacture of textiles. Hemp textiles offer a multiplicity of fabric uses, for bedspreads, blankets, backpacks, carpeting, clothing, draperies, hats, luggage, mattresses, sails, sheets, shoes, shirts, tents, and towels, to name only a few items.

Hemp textiles have a number of advantages over other fabrics. Tests have shown that hemp fibers remain unchanged at heats of nearly 700 degrees. And, according to the Chinese Academy of Sciences, fabrics with at least a 50-percent hemp content block the sun's UV rays more effectively than do other fabrics. Compared to cotton fibers, hemp fibers are longer, stronger, more lustrous and absorbent, and more mildew-resistant. Hemp fabrics also keep the wearer cooler in the summer and warmer in the winter than do cottons or synthetics.

The hemp-textile industry is developing yarn that is lighter-weight and more uniform than what is currently available. This will allow for the much-anticipated

A briefcase made of Hungarian hemp, manufactured in the U.S.

manufacture of hemp T-shirts. Still another way of making fine textiles from hemp is now being rediscovered in Europe. The "cottonization" process converts long, thick hemp fibers into cotton-like bundles that can then be processed in existing spinning and weaving equipment.

4

Today's Hemp Industry

Many of the world's major industrialized countries are presently expanding their hemp industries in order to reap enormous economic and environmental benefits. The following is an overview of the current status of hemp production around the world. In addition to those nations covered, Egypt, India, Portugal, Thailand, and the Ukraine produce hemp, as do most former Soviet Bloc countries.

Australia

While hemp is currently banned, government officials have permitted one farmer to grow the crop on a small-scale research plot. Public support for hemp farming is gathering. An informative, one-hour Australian TV documentary, *The Billion-Dollar Crop*, is available on video. The Tasmanian Hemp Company is campaigning for the legalization of hemp in the State of Tasmania, and the Northern Tasmanian Pulp and Paper Mill is researching possible uses of hemp pulp for their factory.

Canada

Canada was a major hemp-growing region until the 20th century, when that country followed in America's footsteps by prohibiting hemp production. In 1994, Canada issued its first license in over 40 years to Hempline, Inc., which was allowed to plant 10 acres of industrial hemp in the Province of Ontario, on land that previously had been cultivated for tobacco. Dozens of hemp manufacturers and retail stores, supplied by hemp importation, are sprouting up across Canada. Agricultural Canada, the federal agricultural department of Canada, published in December of 1994 their *Bi-weekly Bulletin* Vol. 7, No. 23, on hemp farming, and printed it on hemp paper. Legislation has been introduced by the ruling Liberal Party to lift the ban on industrial hemp,

Hempline, Inc., used a simple tractor and mower for the first hemp harvest in North America since the late 1950s at their 10-acre test plot in Ontario, Canada. (Photo: Geof G. Kime © 1994)

so that farmers throughout Canada can be licensed to grow it. Plans are being developed to establish hemp-processing plants for the anticipated crops.

China

China has been growing hemp (*ma* in Chinese) for at least 6,000 years, and is currently the world's largest exporter of hemp paper and textiles. With its vast natural resources and labor pool, this country will be a major influence in the future hemp industry. China is also the largest producer of nonwood paper, including hemp paper, in the world.

France

In France, over 10,000 tons of industrial hemp (in French, *chanvre*) were harvested in 1994. Kimberly-Clark Corporation manufactures specialty hemp papers, including Bible and cigarette papers, in this Gallic country. French companies are also experimenting with combining hemp fibers and lime to make a lightweight natural cement that can also be used as plaster.

Germany

Since the German ban on the farming of hemp or *hanf* in 1982, there has been little activity until recently. The last German hemp grower farmed 350 acres, selling the fiber to manufacturers of ropes, textiles, and cigarette papers, and the inner stem (or hurds) for conversion into particle board and insulation material. Hemp has

been grown for research purposes at the Agricultural Research Laboratory in Braunschweig since
1992. The 1993 publication in Germany of *The
Rediscovery of the Resource Hemp, Cannabis Marijuana*, by Herer, Brockers, Katalyse, helped
spark renewed interest in the media and gen-
eral public. The German Association of Farmers
has come out in support of the reintroduction of
hemp for cultivation. Many German firms are
developing technologies and products based on
imported hemp. Total 1994 sales for hemp products are estimated to
surpass DM 20 million (U.S. $14 million), up from virtually zero in
1993, according to the nova Institute of Cologne. The Hanfhaus (or
Hemphouse) is a seven-store chain specializing in hemp products.
In 1993, Schneidersohne, Germany's largest paper manufacturer,
introduced a line of hemp-based paper products. In 1995, a remod-
eled pulp mill capable of producing 6,000 tons of hemp and flax
pulp will open near Dresden. Bioresource Hemp, the first hemp
product and technology symposium in the world, was held in Frank-
furt, Germany, in March of 1995.

Great Britain

In 1993, the English Home Office lifted the British
prohibition against hemp farming. More than 30
farmers in England and Scotland have subse-
quently planted industrial hemp. The hemp hurds
are used primarily for animal bedding. Hemcore and
ESP Hemp UK are currently developing markets for
hemp paper and textiles. The United Kingdom's
hemp industry recently received a boost with a £100,000 (U.S.
$150,000) grant from the government to develop new markets for
natural fibers, including hemp and flax.

rope • rugs • sails • salad oils • salves • sandals

One of Hemcore's English hemp farms, taken in Essex (photo © 1993 by Ed Rosenthal).

Hungary

Before the collapse of the Eastern Bloc, Hungary was a major supplier of hemp (*kender*) rope, twine, and textiles to the Soviet Union. The Hungarians are currently rebuilding their hemp-textile industry, and are exporting hemp fabric, much of it to the United States.

Netherlands

The Dutch government is participating in an extensive four-year study to evaluate and test the practical aspects of growing hemp (*hennep*) and processing it into pulp for paper production. A

The Kenderfono hemp twine factory in Szegad, Hungary (photo © 1993 by Ed Rosenthal).

shirts • shoelaces • shoes • skirts • slippers •

respected Dutch researcher, Hayo van der Werf, has written an up-to-date treatise on hemp cultivation, entitled *The Crop Physiology of Fibre Hemp*. The cultivation of hemp is increasing in the Netherlands, along with the development of processing equipment.

Poland

Poland, along with Russia, the Ukraine, and other former Soviet states, currently grows hemp (*penek*) for fabric and manufactures hemp particle-board products for construction.

Romania

Romania is currently the largest commercial producer of hemp in Europe. The total acreage devoted to the crop in 1993 was 40,000 acres. Much of the harvest is currently exported to Hungary for processing before its ultimate exportation to the West.

Russia

Until the 1900s, Russia was the world's largest cultivator and exporter of hemp (*konopli*), employing much of its large peasant labor force in that industry. The N.I. Vavilov Scientific Research Institute of Plant Industry (VIR)

in Saint Petersburg maintains the largest hemp germ plasm collection in the world, one that includes many varieties not found in other gene banks. The International Hemp Association is raising

funds so that the VIR can continue to plant and maintain these irre-
placeable hemp seeds.

Slovenia
Slovenia is growing hemp, and its currency-printing
plant also manufactures hemp paper for exportation to
the United States.

Spain
In Spain, hemp is known as *cañamo*. Spain
is currently the sole exporter of hemp
pulp for specialty papers. The country's
domestic hemp products include rope and
textiles.

The United States
The U.S. government has not granted any permits for large-scale
hemp farming in over 40 years. In fact, in recent years the Smith-
sonian Institute in Washington, DC, removed tags identifying
Early-American textile relics in their museum as hemp products.
However, increasing interest among Americans in using environmentally friendly products has created a growing demand for hemp
goods. Also, based on legal research, it is the opinion of experts
that individual states have the right to allow farmers to plant industrial hemp. Although in early 1992 there were less than a dozen
active hemp importers and manufacturers in the United States, by
1994 over 200 firms were offering a wide range of hemp products.
Successful start-ups are surpassing the one-million-dollar mark for
annual sales, with total annual hemp-product sales estimated to be
in the tens of millions of dollars. Large corporations are developing
exciting new products to be marketed in major department stores.
Given the renewed public interest and the fact that supplies are still

● support beams ● T-shirts ● tablecloths ● tables

limited (essentially, all raw and processed materials must be imported), costs are artificially high. Over the next several years, the law of supply and demand will increase supplies while bringing prices down. Government decisions on whether to lift the hemp ban in Canada and/or the U.S. will greatly affect markets. If Canada is the first North American country to legalize hemp, U.S. farmers will question why they are being prevented from growing the crop. When either country lifts its ban, large quantities of industrial hemp will be available domestically within only a few years, eliminating the high transportation costs of imported hemp goods. In November of 1994, the Governor of Kentucky appointed a task force to evaluate the feasibility of tobacco farmers growing hemp. And, in January of 1995, the Hemp Production Act of 1995 was introduced in the Colorado state legislature. These are hopeful signs that governments within the United States are starting to recognize hemp's potential.

5

Job and Business Opportunities

The demand for hemp products is increasing as more people look for high-quality, longer-lasting goods, manufactured in an environmentally responsible manner. International corporations are downsizing, thus encouraging people to turn to smaller-scale jobs and business opportunities. Today's top-selling business books promote ethical and spiritual business practices, along with "corporate greening." Hemp offers numerous fields (see chart at left) in which hardworking entrepreneurs can create profitable new businesses.

Hemp can supply the products that will allow us to live comfortably in the 21st century, while offering significant opportunities in areas that include farming, processing, manufacturing, retailing, and cooperatives. Countries such as England, Hungary, and Germany are already developing new jobs by expanding their hemp industries.

Hemp's 25,000 commodities will positively impact major worldwide industries:

- agriculture
- construction materials
- cosmetics
- food
- furniture
- industrial resins
- paper
- plastics
- recycling
- retailing
- textiles

Bioregional Economics

The term "bioregional" describes a biological region based on natural land boundaries, such as a valley or river basin. The goal of bioregional economics is to stimulate economic activity that is beneficial to both people and the ecology. The ability of hemp to grow in most climates, as well as its amazing product versatility, perfectly suits it to bioregional economics.

> *Producing goods for local use benefits the local job and tax base, whereas importing the same goods from thousands of miles away does not.*

Rural economies will receive a boost as hemp manufacturers and processors reduce transportation costs by locating their operations close to large hemp-growing regions, and the number of new jobs will grow as the hemp industry grows.

Where Have Your Blue Jeans Been?

Let's compare the effects of purchasing a pair of locally manufactured blue jeans versus buying one from across the globe.

The local farmer grows some hemp, and sells it to a regional processor who offers good-paying jobs. The processor markets the resulting hemp textiles to a local garment factory, where a pair of hemp jeans is made. These jeans are then resold at a local, family-owned retail store. The net effect of this sequence of events (the growing, processing, manufacture, and retailing all in one region) helps the local economy by creating jobs and circulating currency within the community. Thus the wearer of these jeans contributes to the well-being of his or her bioregion.

Meanwhile, the cotton farmer, under pressure from an international textile company to reduce prices, increases the use of

This is fine fiber derived from hemp stalks.

chemicals to try to boost yields, thereby polluting the groundwater. The textile company manufactures a pair of jeans from that cotton, and ships them thousands of miles across the sea. Upon their reaching the country of import, further transportation is required. The quantity of petroleum used in moving such goods around the world is phenomenal. To meet this demand, major oil companies are drilling for oil in the world's rain forests, where repeated oil spills kill fish, harming indigenous tribes.

While international trade will always play an important role in our lives, communities can positively influence local economic outcomes. Regions where factories will be shut down due to the impact of global trade agreements can effectively "weatherize their economic houses" against financial storms by pursuing bioregional economic strategies. A growing number of informed farmers, workers, and business people are ready and able to develop a strong hemp industry that will benefit not only their own and their children's lives, but their communities as well.

6

The Next Step

Given the influence of the United States in the economy of the global village, it follows that trends in the U.S. hemp industry will positively impact economic trends throughout the world. Of course, what happens in other countries will influence these trends as well. Canada, Australia, and Germany, which currently restrict hemp production, nevertheless are working to develop their respective hemp industries. All have government-approved research plots and increasing public support to lift the hemp ban. In coming years, Free Market traders will continue to jump over the U.S. "Hemp Wall" to deliver imported hemp products.

Purchasers of hemp products are voting with their dollars, and the race is on to market ecological goods to this expanding group of buyers. The following are three possible future scenarios for the U.S. hemp industry.

The Burro-Wearing-Blinders Scenario

In this scenario, the burro is slow to move. Elected officials, timid in the face of uncertain political times, choose the familiar policy of status quo, and the hemp industry is prevented from making optimal progress. Since government is less afraid of the tobacco industry than of hemp, conversion from tobacco to hemp is considerably slowed. Anti-drug laws (which still, through public ignorance, influence hemp production) are strengthened. Hemp farming in other countries, including Canada, is slow to develop.

Yet, over time, fiber shortages in the Pacific Northwest, combined with steady hemp importation, force the government's hand. When hemp is finally recognized as a means of reducing the trade deficit, the last barrier is removed. Farmers are licensed to grow hemp early in the 21st century.

The Draft-Horse Scenario

The draft horse moves at a steady pace. Shifting political and economic winds create opportunities for bold and ambitious policymakers. Research projects in Wisconsin, Oregon, and Kentucky are proposed for evaluation. In 1996, several test plots are approved, and hemp products imported from Canada and Europe approach $100 million in annual retail sales. An official protocol for licensing hemp growers is developed and, in the spring of 1998, thousands of farmers plant hemp.

The Thoroughbred Scenario

The thoroughbred is very fast—a strong contender in any race. The State of Kentucky decides not to wait for the federal government to find a solution for the tobacco farmer. With such state governments providing leadership, bureaucratic roadblocks are removed and several hemp farmers receive licenses by the end of 1995. This encourages other states to undertake trial research in 1996. By 1997, hemp fields are planted in 30 states. Innovation in processing technology for textiles, paper, and fiberboard is demonstrated on a wide industrial scale. The United States becomes a leader in the worldwide hemp industry.

Of these possible scenarios, that of the draft horse appears the most likely, while the thoroughbred scenario is moving up fast. Eventually, even in the burro-with-blinders scenario, farmers, business people, and aware citizens will demand that the unreasonable ban on hemp production be lifted.

● weed suppression ● window blinds ● wood stains ●

A sower of hemp (source: The Reign of Law: A Tale of the Kentucky Hemp Fields, James Allen, 1900).

Sowing Seeds of Hope

Each one of us can accelerate this process by taking personal action. If you have found this book informative, you can help to increase the number of industrial-hemp advocates by sending a copy to a friend, colleague, or family member. Consider writing a letter to your local newspaper editor or making a presentation to a community group. People are very receptive to hearing about new job and business opportunities that will also benefit the environment. If you want to learn more, the resources listed on the following page may be helpful. Also, please contact HEMPTECH to inquire about forthcoming publications, including our series of *Hemp Reports*.

Glossary

bast fibers: The long fibers present in the outer portions of hemp stalks. Historically, bast fibers have been used for the manufacturing of textiles and paper.

bioregional economics: The practices of communities that value and encourage local enterprises healthy for the people, the economy, and the environment of their region.

bleaching: The process of whitening paper pulp to obtain a bright-looking sheet of paper. Almost all wood-pulp mills use a bleaching process that deposits acids, chlorine, sulfur, and dioxins into the environment.

composites: Industrial substances such as fiberboard, made up of various elements such as binders and the woody fiber from trees or hemp.

decorticating machine: A hemp-processing machine first invented around the turn of the 20th century to separate hemp bark from the hurds. This machine allowed the previously unused 80 percent of the hemp stalk (or hurds) to be converted into a raw material from which thousands of different products are made, and also dramatically reduced labor costs.

essential fatty acids: The "good" or polyunsaturated fats found in certain fishes and plants, termed "essential" because they cannot be synthesized by the human body and must be included in the diet for good health.

hemp fiber: A product extracted from the stalk of the hemp plant and used to make a wide range of paper and textile products.

hemp hurds: The short-fiber core portion of the hemp-plant stalk.

hemp seed: The seeds of the hemp plant, which contain approximately 25 percent protein and have an oil content of 25 to 30 percent.

hemp seed cake: The portion of the seed that remains after the oil has been extracted; an excellent food source for human or animal consumption.

hydrogen peroxide: An environmentally friendly bleaching substance used for processing fiber such as hemp into useable pulp.

industrial hemp: A variety of *Cannabis sativa L.*, a tall annual herb of the mulberry family, native to Asia. The plant is grown for a wide range of consumer and industrial products, and possesses no psychoactive qualities.

kenaf: A tall annual of the hibiscus family, native to Africa and grown in warmer climates. The plant is used for various consumer and industrial products.

low-THC seed varieties: Hemp seeds that will grow plants with no psychoactive properties. These varieties range from less than 0.3 percent (the European Economic Community standard) to one percent in their delta-9 tetrahydrocannabinol (THC) content.

pulping: The process of extracting woody pulp from fiber. In comparison to wood pulping, hemp pulping uses considerably fewer chemicals, due to its lower lignin content.

stalk: The woody, fibrous portion of the hemp plant. Stalks are harvested after 70 to 100 days when they are 6 to 16 feet tall, for processing into two major elements: fiber and hurds.

tree-free: A term used to describe products made without the use of trees. For example, hemp, flax, cotton, and kenaf are used to make tree-free paper.

ORDER FORM

If your favorite retailer or catalog is sold out of Industrial Hemp, *use the following order form.*

✳ **Fax orders:** (805) 646-7404

☎ **Telephone orders:** Call Toll-Free 24 hours: (800) 265-HEMP
    M/C and Visa accepted.

✉ **Postal orders:** Make check payable to Publication Services*, P.O.
    Box 820-900, Ojai, CA 93024-0820, USA

? **Inquiries:** Telephone (805) 646-HEMP

                                                    * *Fulfillment house for HEMPTECH*

Price
$4.95 per book

Sales tax
Please add 7.25% for books shipped to California addresses

Airmail shipping
$3.50 first book, $2.00 each additional book

Payment
❑ Check   ❑ Visa   ❑ Mastercard

Card number _____

Name on card _____ Expiration date _____

Number of books ordered _____   Amount enclosed _____

Company Name _____

Name and Title _____

Address _____

City _____ State _____ Zip _____

Telephone (_____) _____

❑ *Please send a flyer on hemp publications.*